いきもののうた
Impressions of Living Things

公益財団法人JAL財団＝編
Edited by JAL Foundation

ブロンズ新社
Bronze Publishing

世界の子どもたちによるハイク

初代EU大統領　日本EU俳句友好交流大使　ヘルマン・ファンロンパイ

近年、世界中でハイクをたしなむ人が増えています。私のにもへも学校単位で作品が送られてくることがあり、そのたびにまぶしい才能に出会っています。何よりも嬉しいのは、子どもたちが心情を見事に表現している点です。ハイクは目や耳を敏感にし、心を研ぎ澄ませてくれます。慌ただしい世の中でふと立ち止まり、自分自身を意識しながら生きる手助けにもなります。幼少期にこうした術を学んでおけば、いつまでもその気持ちを持ち続けていられるでしょう。

地球上のどこにいても、生や死、悲しみや喜びを経験します。さまざまな国を訪れる中で、私が最も強く心を打たれたのは、違いよりも共通点でした。どうしても違う点ばかりに目を向けがちですが、私たちは実は一つであり、それこそが平和へと繋がるのだと思います。自分の国を愛すると同時に、誰もがよい生活や幸せに憧れていることをどうか忘れないでください。ハイクには怒りや妬みといった否定的な感情に負けない、前向きなエネルギーを生みだす力があるのです。

ハイクは、たった三行の短い詩です。誰にでも作れると思われがちですが、よりよい句を作るためには、集中力を高め、シンプルな単語に置き換えなければなりません。しかしながら、はじめのうちは細かいことは気にしないでください。学びとは、いつでもゆっくり進むもの。言葉で遊びながら、まずは日常を簡潔に表現してみましょう。

大切なのは、子どもたちが夢中になることですから、大人は決して教えすぎてはいけません。古代ギリシャに「神はあなたの中にいる」という言葉があるように、ハイクにおいても神聖なる自然や宇宙は自らの内にあり、技術は後からついてくるからです。心に語らせたら、すべて自然の成り行きに任せましょう。どんなにベテランの俳人でも、若い方たちの句を読むと新たな発見があるものです。私も、彼らの熱意に触れるたびにパワーをもらっています。

日本で誕生した俳句は、今や世界中に広がりました。この『地球歳時記』は希望の一冊です。子どもたちの想像力や夢、そして絵が私たちに大切なことを教えてくれます。この本の出版は、偉大なる第一歩なのです。実は最近、第二代国連事務総長であるダグ・ハマーショルド氏のお墓参りに行きました。彼は世界平和を目指す最も重要な役割を果たしたと同時に、すばらしい俳人でもありました。彼の平和への献身と八イクに対する想いは、密接に関係していたと私は考えています。ハイクを通して、平和を求める心も育っていくのです。

* 「ハイク」：日本語の五七五で詠まれる「俳句」に対し、海外の母国語で詠まれる三行の詩を「ハイク」と表現しています。

はじめに

Haiku by World Children

Herman Van Rompuy
President Emeritus European Council
Japan/EU Haiku Friendship Ambassador

Since it has become well known that I am a haiku poet, a lot of people in Belgium and elsewhere are trying to compose haiku. It often happens that schools send me tens of poems made by their pupils. Each time I discover real talents. But I'm most happy that children are expressing their emotions and their observations about small things at their home or at school. It sharpens their eyes and ears, their hearts and their minds. It helps to live in a more conscious way in our hasty world. Writing a haiku is pressing a pause button. When you learn that behaviour in your childhood, there is a chance that you keep that spirit later. Haiku can be part of an educational project.

Children all over the world can participate at this contest. The 17 syllables of haiku can be written in almost every language. The experiences in nature also are almost the same. Everywhere there is a sunrise and a sunset, life and death, sorrow and joy etc. Human beings are basically the same. Traveling all over the world, I am more struck by the similarities instead of our differences. We attach to much importance to the latter. We should emphasise what binds us. That is the royal way to peace. You should love your country and your region but you should never forget that we all are human beings with the same longings for a good life and for happiness. Haiku poets are developing positive energy as a antidote to all those negative feelings such as anger, jealousy, enemy-thinking, revenge etc. Haiku has a moral vocation.

Haiku is a short poem. It makes it accessible to many people, also children. But the art of writing a good haiku is more complicated than it seems. We have to focus our attention and to look for the shortest way to translate it into words. It's a matter of concentration. But in the early stages of learning haiku, one should be indulgent. Learning is always a gradual process. Let the kids first play with words. Let them write about every day life in the most simple way. Learning by doing.

In this exercise the teachers should not teach too much. Enthusiasm is the first prerequisite. In old Greek language it means that God is in you. In the haiku philosophy it means that the sacred nature and cosmos are in you. The technique follows later. Let the heart speak first. All the rest is a natural consequence of it. Beauty is the best professor. Older haiku poets can recharge by reading poems of their younger colleagues. Enthusiasm is a prerogative of the youngsters. I become enthusiastic when I see enthusiasm! It is contagious.

Haiku is a Japanese creation but it became global. This 'global haiku' found its way to this anthology, also full of drawings. It is a book of hope. The imagination, the dreams, the wording and the drawings let us see how we once were and what we have to reconquer to some extent. The publication of this book is a great initiative, for the moral and educational reasons I mentioned. A world of poets is a better world. I recently visited the grave of the greatest of all secretary-general of the United Nations, the most important organisation for peace in the world. This man, Dag Hammarskjold was a haiku poet. I'm convinced that his commitment to peace had a direct link with his poetry. Learning by example.

August 2018

1章 みんななかま
All Our Friends

ここはジャングルだ
いっぱい動物がいる
みんな一緒に暮らしてる

This is a jungle
There are many animals
They are living together

M. Pethmin Sasen Rodrigo
age10　Male　Sri Lanka（スリランカ）

鳥の歌
私に感じさせる
生きているって

The song of birds
Makes me feel
Alive

Песента на птиците
Кара ме да се чувствам
Жива

Десислава Цветанова Димитрова
Desislava Tsvetanova Dimitrova
age15　Female
Bulgaria（ブルガリア）

On the silver-white snow
There are angels dancing with their wings
To praise the peace in the world

銀白雪地裡
舞動天使的翅膀
歌頌人間吉祥

張 子菲
Chang Tzu-Fei
age12　Female
Taiwan（台湾／台北）

白銀の雪の上で
翼で踊る天使たち
世界の平和をたたえて

Birds soar through the sky
Migrating for the winter
As the gold sun sets

Charlotte Tham
age10　Female
Singapore（シンガポール）

高い空を飛ぶ
冬の渡り鳥
金色の夕日が沈む

A seagull flies
In the blue rectangle
Of my window

Galeb leti
U plavom pravokutniku
Moga prozora

Ela Makić Halilčevic
Ela Makic Halilcevic
age 8　Female
Croatia（クロアチア）

カモメが飛ぶ
青くて四角い
わたしの窓

Seamlessly moving
Leaving paw prints in the snow
A burning red glow

Felix Dewsnap
age11　Female
UK（英国）

なめらかに動いて
雪に足あとを残す
燃える赤い輝き

I am king of forest
Protecting green and fresh woods
Lives keep breeding

Ta là chúa sơn lâm
Bảo vệ khắp khu rừng xanh tốt
Sự sống luôn sinh sôi

Lưu Bảo Khôi
Luu Bao Khoi
age12　Male
Vietnam（ベトナム）

ぼくは森林の王
緑の若い木々を守る
生命をつなぐため

Some are predators
Some are slow and some are fast
Some live in oceans

Orion Hall
age 7　Male
USA（米国／ダラス）

肉食もいるし
のろいのも速いのもいる
海で暮らすのもいるよ

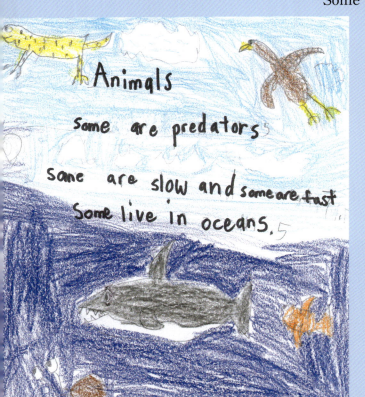

いろんな仲間
近寄ってお互いを知り
仲良くなる

Different kind of company
Gets to know each other by moving closer
Involved together

另類的伙伴
彼此靠近相互刺探
同樣的羈絆

朱 庭儀
Chu Ting-Yi
age12　Female
Taiwan（台湾／台北）

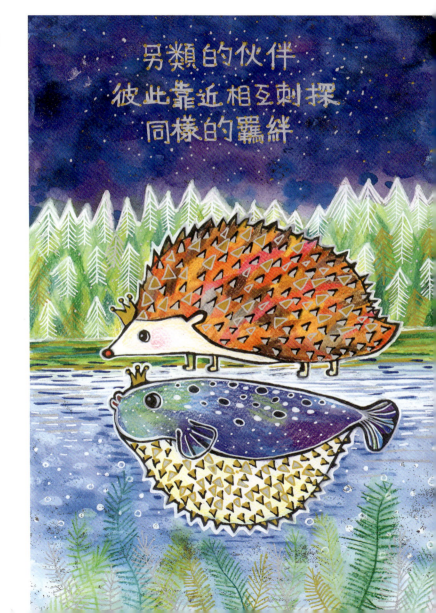

A falcon flies south
A silhouette in the sky
Gliding toward the sun

Akio Calvin Richard Freauff
age10　Male
USA（米国／サンディエゴ）

ハヤブサは南へ
太陽に向かってすべるように飛ぶ
空のシルエット

In an oak's hollow
A fox hides its young
Only eyes peeking

U dublju hrasta
Lisica sakrila mlade
Samo oči vire

Antonio Frljužec
Antonio Frljuzec
age12　Male
Croatia（クロアチア）

樫の木の穴に
キツネは子どもをかくす
目だけが覗いてる

The rain began to fall
Flying ants fly
The lizard happy

Hujan Datang
Laron Terbang
Cicak Senang

Muhammad Alive Muflih
age14　Male
Indonesia（インドネシア）

雨が降りはじめて
羽アリが飛ぶ
喜ぶトカゲ

A horse race
A cat on the fence
Observing a white horse

Tekma konjičkov
Muca z ograje gleda
belega konja

Nastja Marčič
age 7　Female
Slovenia（スロベニア）

お馬のレース
柵の上の猫が
白馬を見ている

Mother bird
Feeding her baby birds
How nice to see

माउले चारो
बचेरालाई खुवायो
हामी रमायौ

अनुज्ञ नेपाल
Anugya Nepal
age14　Female
Nepal（ネパール）

母鳥がひな鳥にエサを私もうれしい

Freezing sound
On this fine winter day
Bird takes off

Pakkanen paukkuu
on ihana talvisää
Lintu lennähtää

Eeva Kari
age14　Female
Finland（フィンランド）

凍る音晴れた冬の日に鳥が飛びたつ

Watching the distance
Carrying summer away
Cranes are flying off

Смотрю в даль
Унося лето с собой
Летят журавли

Jekaterina Krupnova
age14　Female
Latvia（ラトビア）

遠くを見わたすと夏を連れてツルが飛んでいく

Little owl
Wakes up at night to find its friends
To count the stars together

小小貓頭鷹
夜裏醒來找朋友
一起數星星

蕭 卓希
Siu Cheuk Hei Matt
age11　Male
China（中国／香港）

小さなフクロウ夜中に起きて友を誘う一緒に星を数えよう

On a clear afternoon
A gecko on the red brick wall has nothing to do
The breeze brushes the wall lightly

晴朗的午後
沒事做的壁虎停在紅磚牆壁上
微風輕拂在牆上

李 翊綸
Li Yi-Lun
age10　Female
Taiwan（台湾／台北）

よく晴れた午後
赤煉瓦に手もちぶさたのヤモリ
壁をなでるそよ風

Forgotten road
In the auto light
Running ears

Pamirštas kelias
Automobilio šviesoj
Bėgančios ausys

忘れられた道
車のライトに
逃げる耳

Matas Zajauskas
age14　Male
Lithuania（リトアニア）

I trot everyday
With my friend on my back
And like cats and hay

Lorraine O'Shea
age13　Female
Ireland（アイルランド）

毎日はや足で駆ける
友だちを背中に乗せて
猫と干し草が好き

The elephant's trunk
Wants to get over the fence
Lingering day

ぞうのはな
さくをでたがる
ひながかな

西田 咲笑
Sae Nishida
age 9　Female
Japan（日本）

My rabbit found
A small ball and carrots
He hid the carrots

Mój królik znalazł
Piłeczkę i marchewki
Schował marchewki

Dominika Musiał
age 8　Female
Poland（ポーランド）

わたしのウサギが見つけた
小さなボールとニンジン
そしてニンジンをかくしたの

Softness of a cushion
Rabbit with beige hairs
Joy of a caress

Douceur d'un coussin
Le lapin aux poils beiges
Joie d'une caresse

Wayne Fatimata
age 7　Female
France（フランス）

やわらかいクッション
ベージュ色の毛のウサギ
なでるのうれしい

渡り鳥のフラミンゴ
雲へ宇宙へ歩む
影が湖にうつる

Migratory flamingos
Walk into cloud, into space
Shadows reflect into the lake

Đoàn hồng hạc di cư
Lội mây, lội cả vào vũ trụ
Hồ nước trong in bóng

Trần Thanh Ngân
Tran Thanh Ngan
age14　Female
Vietnam（ベトナム）

Cold morning
A sparrow is eating
The seeds of sunflower

Fría Mañana
Un gorrión comiendo
Pipas del girasol

Pablo Tébar Medina
age11　Male
Spain（スペイン）

寒い朝
一羽のスズメが
ヒマワリの種をつついている

As everyone knows
The early bird gets the worm
Slurp, slurp one by one

Tong Wan Ying
age10　Female
Singapore（シンガポール）

みんなが知っているように
早起き鳥はミミズをつかまえて
順番にムシャムシャ

Full moon
A little bird on the bare branch
And the same old song

Пълна луна
Малка птичка на голия клон
И същата стара песен

満月
裸の枝に小鳥
いつもの懐かしい歌

Рая Венкова Моянкова
Raya Venkova Moyankova
age 13　Female
Bulgaria（ブルガリア）

A grey peregrine
Quickly descends
And sees very well

Siv sokol selec
Se zelo hitro spušča
In dobro vidi

灰色のハヤブサ
すばやく降りて
とても目がいい

Galen Gaberšček
age 7　Male
Slovenia（スロベニア）

Flying joyfully
Over the hills, as they sing
Graceful voices, birds

楽しそうに飛びながら
丘を越えて歌えば
すてきな声の鳥たち

Audrey Lin
age 11　Female
USA（米国／サンディエゴ）

Winter birds
Fly together
With snowflakes

Žiemos paukščiai
Skrenda kartu
Su snaigėmis

ふゆのとり
とんでいるよ
ゆきといっしょに

Rusnė Rimšelytė
Rusne Rimselyte
age 5　Female
Lithuania（リトアニア）

アヒルが川(かわ)で泳(およ)いでいる
チョウが飛(と)びまわっている
アヒルの子(こ)が母(かあ)さんの後(あと)をついていく

The ducks are swimming in the river
The butterflies are flying
The duckling is going after the mother duck

T.G. Noshika Ganguli
age10　Female
Sri Lanka（スリランカ）

火山の爆発が止み
新しい生命が生まれた
永遠に続く幸せの音

A volcano eruption has ended
Giving way to new life
Endless sound of happiness

펑펑 터지던 화산이 멈추어
생명이 태어났네
무한한 행복의 소리

이 호준
Lee Hojun
age12　Male
Korea（韓国）

Wolves howl
And hedgehogs sleep quietly
Hibernating, dreaming

Hundid uluvad
Siilid magavad vaikselt
Oma talveund

Sandra Roos
age 9　Female
Estonia（エストニア）

オオカミが吠える
ハリネズミは静かに冬眠
夢を見ながら

The cat felt cold
White rushed after white
The houses made a tent

Kedi üşüdü
Beyaz beyaza koştu
Evler kamp kurdu

Eylül Yener
age 8　Female
Turkey（トルコ）

猫がこごえる
白と白がまざって
屋根はテントみたいだ

The cat sleeping
In his wool bed
And he snores

El gato duerme
En su cama de lana
Y el roncaba

Ariadna Guadalupe Morales Miendeta
age 9　Female
Mexico（メキシコ）

猫が寝てる
ウールのベッドで
いびきをかきながら

Under the moonlight
In that bright forest
A white wolf

Bajo la luna
En aquel bosque claro
Un lobo blanco

Carolina Guantes Domínguez
age12　Female
Spain（スペイン）

月明かりの下
あの明るい森に
一匹の白いオオカミ

Baby snake
Breaks egg shell
I love it

सर्पको बच्चा
मलाई मन पर्यो
अण्डा फुटेर

सुशान्त न्यौपाने
Sushant Neupane
age14　Male
Nepal（ネパール）

殻をやぶって
出てきたヘビの子
大好きだ

The animals play
The sun is shining brightly
I love the summer

Roísín Beazley
age 8　Female
Ireland（アイルランド）

動物たちが遊び
お日さまが明るく輝いている
わたしは夏が好き

Look over there
The flying goldfinches
Beautiful all of them

Olha para ali
Os pintassilgos que voam
Lindos todos eles

Eliane Augusta Monteiro Semedo
age15　Female
Portugal（ポルトガル）

ごらん
ゴシキヒワが飛んでいく
みんなとても美しい

夜明けが
灰色の猫をてらす
来る日も来る日も

The dawn of day
Reflecting on the grey cat
Every day

El alba del sol
Refleja en el gato gris
Todos los días

Irene Ochando Jiménez
age11　Female
Spain（スペイン）

Martin-blue fisherman
Plunge in the glowing sun
Beautiful winter sun

Martin - pêcheur bleu
Plonge au soleil rougeoyant
Beau soleil d'hiver

Rin Okayasu
age13　Female
Senegal（セネガル）

翡翠色のカワセミが
赤々と燃えるお日さまに飛びこむ
冬の美しい太陽に

Outside fishes swim
Birds fly there and people walk
I sit inside

Buiten zwemmen vissen
Er vliegen vogels en er lopen mensen
Ik zit binnen

Noor Baljeu
age12　Female
Netherlands（オランダ）

外では魚が泳ぎ
鳥は飛び 人が歩いている
私は家のなか

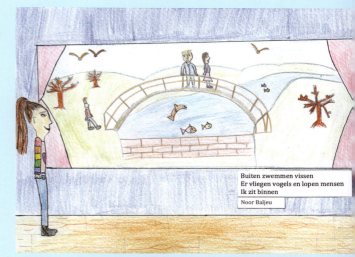

Evening is coming
A wolf goes for a walk
Wow! Swallowed up glasses...

Vakaras ateina
Eina vilkas pasivaikščioti
Šast! Ir prarijo akinius...

Egilija Rimkutė
Egilija Rimkute
age10　Female
Lithuania（リトアニア）

夜になると
オオカミは散歩にいく
あれ、メガネをのみこんだ

A wild wolf
Howling at the moon
Nature

Salvaje lobo
Aullando a la luna
Naturaleza

Ana Torres Molina
age 9　Female
Spain（スペイン）

野生のオオカミ
月に向かって吠えている
自然

With my horse
Trotting in the beautiful green grass
Leave or stay?

Avec mon cheval
Au trot dans les beaux prés verts
Partir ou rester?

Glan Orlane
age 8　Female
France（フランス）

馬に乗って
きれいな緑の野原を行く？
行く？それともここにいる？

A white horse
Dry corn
Is blown by the wind

Bijeli konj
Suho žito
Otpuhuje vjetar

Marko Šepić
Marko Sepic
age 13　Male
Croatia（クロアチア）

一頭の白い馬
乾いた穀草が
風に吹かれている

わくわくと
のったせなかは
あったかい

Trembling with joy
I mount its back
The warmth

布川 千夏
Chika Nunokawa
age 9　Female
Japan（日本）

Stretches lazily
Purring in bright pink blossom
Tabby peering down

Joshua Das
age 9　Male
UK（英国）

のんびりのびをして
ピンクの花(はな)のなかでのどをゴロゴロ
トラ猫(ねこ)がのぞいてるよ

Lunar Rabbit
Forest of your stars
Lights of my dreams

Conejo Lunar
Bosque de tus estrellas
Luz de mis sueños

Luna Anais Campos Ruiz
age13　Female
Mexico（メキシコ）

月(つき)のウサギ
あなたの星(ほし)の森(もり)
私(わたし)の夢(ゆめ)の明(あ)かり

Hi, rabbits!
You are wearing
Blankets all the time

久保 架心
Kako Kubo
age 3　Female
Japan（日本）

うさぎさん
いつももうふを
まとってる

Staring down today
"OK" just enough to finally
Catch up with my tail

Hannah Tang
age11　Female
Singapore（シンガポール）

今日(きょう)もにらんで
よし、やっと
シッポに届(とど)いた

My wings
Like soaring in the sky
Without nothing

Бодлын тэнгэрт
Далавчгүй дүүлэх
Миний жигүүр

Бямбадорж Дөлгөөн-Эрдэнэ
Byambadorj Dulguun-Erdene
age 9　Male
Mongolia（モンゴル）

ぼくの翼
空高く舞いあがるようだ
何も持たずに

Colorful flowers and trees
Panda, panda
Sitting alone black and white

Rừng cây muôn ngàn sắc hoa lá
Gấu trúc, gấu trúc
Giản đơn đen trắng ngồi một mình

Nguyễn Gia Linh
Nguyen Gia Linh
age12　Female
Vietnam（ベトナム）

色鮮やかな花や葉
パンダ、パンダ
ひとりで座る黒と白

Grandma on the path
An apple rolled
Under the horse's feet

Babcia na ścieżce
Potoczyło się jabłko
Pod nogi konia

Zuzanna Formanowska
age 7　Female
Poland（ポーランド）

道におばあさん
リンゴが転がる
馬の脚の下

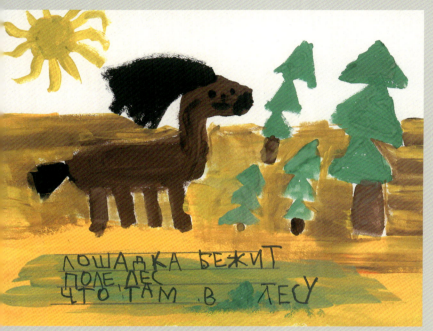

A horse galloping
Meadow changes to forest
What awaits inside

Лошадка бежит
Поле лес
Что там в лесу

Darja Giņko
Darja Ginko
age 5　Female
Latvia（ラトビア）

うまがはしる
のはらがもりにかわる
なにがまっているのかな

Breeze in summer noon
Little deer whispers to mom
"Mama, look the sky…"

Buổi trưa hè gió mát
Hươu con ghé sát vào hươu mẹ
"Mẹ ơi, bầu trời kia…"

Trần Thục Anh
Tran Thuc Anh
age12　Female
Vietnam（ベトナム）

夏の昼のそよ風
子ジカがささやく
「ママ、空を見て…」

Under an oak
A yellow bird is singing
The sound of the sea

Debajo del roble
Canta un verdon
Al son de la mar

Nuria García Acejo
age11　Female
Spain（スペイン）

ドングリの木の下で
黄色い鳥が歌ってる
海の音

It sings every day
Let it fly to freedom
It is a living creature

Vsak dan mi poje
Naj zleti v svobodo
Je živo bitje

Gregor Klobučar
age10　Male
Slovenia（スロベニア）

毎日歌って
自由へと飛びたつ
それは生きもの

生きものがいると私は幸せ
どの生きものも独特で特別
それは地球の奇跡

Living things make me happy
Every living things are unique and special
It is the miracle of the world

Амьд бүхэн надад аз жаргалыг өгдөг
Ямар ч амьтан цорын ганц давтагдашгүй
Энэ нь дэлхийн гайхамшиг юм

Төмөр Бадмаараг
Tumur Badmaarag
age12　Female
Mongolia（モンゴル）

雨が降って
背の高い草のなかで犬が横たわる
シッポはぐっしょり

Raindrops are falling
In high grass, there lies a dog
Tail completely wet

Līst lietus
Suns izgājis atpūsties zālītē
Mitra aste

Elizabete Brale
age10　Female
Latvia（ラトビア）

カンガルーはここの王さま
バックパックを前につけて
ピョーンピョーン飛びはねる

Kangaroo rules here
With a backpack in the front
Jumping up and down

Chew En Hui, Stephanie
age 7　Female
Singapore（シンガポール）

2章 たいせつないのち
Precious Life

真っ青な夏の空
水中をゆっくり泳ぐコイ
太陽がキラリと光る

Bright blue summer sky
Koi moves slowly through water
Reflection of sun

Drew Hesp
age15　Male　USA（米国／ボストン）

生き物は
みんな ずるがしこい
ときどき なまけものもいるよね

All living things
Are cunning and smart
Some are lazy

Bütün canlılar
Kurnazdır ve akıllı
Bazısı tembel

Emirhan Akyol
age10　Male
Turkey（トルコ）

沈む月
月を取る網を
クモは編む

Falling moon
A spider
Weaves moon-catching web

Trăng rơi xuống
Con nhện
Giăng tơ hứng trăng

Nguyễn Yến Trang
Nguyen Yen Trang
age12　Female
Vietnam（ベトナム）

魚のパウル
新しい年を楽しみに
イェーイと泡を出す

A fish called Paul
Looks forward to the new year
Bubbling hooray

Ein Fisch namens Paul
Freut sich auf das neue Jahr
Und blubbert HURRA

Cornelius Dort
age11　Male
Germany（ドイツ）

Melting frost
The spider web seems
Alabaster

Colare di brina
Appare alabastrina
La ragnatela

Letizia Cisint
age15　Female
Italy（イタリア）

霜がとけて
クモの巣は
アラバスターのよう

The whole world
Finds room in its eyes
Little dragonfly

Будто весь мир
Уместился в ее глазах
Маленькая стрекоза

Анастасия Пилюгина
Anastasia Pilyuginae
age13　Female
Russia（ロシア）

全世界が
その眼のなかに入る
小さなトンボ

Two fish swam in his dish
He blew bubbles
And made a wish

Shivam
age 13　Male
India（インド）

金魚鉢で泳ぐ二匹の魚
あぶくを出して
願いごとをした

Herrings glide and swim
North sea crashes against the wall
Fisherman catches fish

Rafe Dewsnap
age 7　Male
UK（英国）

すいすい泳ぐニシン
がけにぶつかってくだける北の海
漁師は魚をつかまえる

きれいなにじ
じゆうなひは
さかなもうれしそう

So beautiful rainbow
The free day
So happy fish

美丽的彩虹
自由自在的一天
快乐的小鱼

曲 忆菡
Qu Yihan
age 5　Female
China（中国／大連）

I set the fish free
Go home
To your mom

にがしたよ
かあさんとこに
かえってね

宮井 さくら
Sakura Miyai
age 5　Female
Japan（日本）

On the withered grass
Waiting for sunrise
A weary horse

枯草の上で
日の出を待っている
疲れた馬

Mambet Esra
age13　Female
Romania（ルーマニア）

White winter snow
My turtle is afraid of the wind
She takes her salad

Blanche neige d'hiver
Ma tortue a peur du vent
Elle prend sa salade

冬の白い雪
私のカメさん風はこわいが
サラダを食べる

Lebon Shanna
age11　Female
France（フランス）

そよ風
小さな生命が空いっぱい
冷たい風にもおびえずに

Soft wind
Little life flies to the sky
Not surprised at the cold wind

微风吹又吹
小小生命漫天飞
不怕冷风吹

张 欣婕
Zhang Xinjie
age11　Female
China（中国／广州）

Cicadas in the dark
Music among the wheat ears
Short is the night

Cicale nel buio
Musica tra le spighe
Breve è la notte

Emma Palamin
age15　Female
Italy（イタリア）

暗闇のセミ
麦の穂から音楽
短い夜

真夜中に
カエルたちのゲロゲロ
どうやったら眠れるの？

In the middle of the night
The croaking of frogs
How can I sleep?

No meio da noite
O coaxar das rãs
Tem como dormir?

Camila Aparecida Gaiocha
age11　Female
Brazil（ブラジル）

緑色の想い
世界は
二匹の小さなカエルの内に

Green emotion
The world
In two little frogs

Зелена емоция
Светът в
две жабки

Елена Светланова Деянова
Elena Svetlanova Deyanova
age13　Female
Bulgaria（ブルガリア）

Raising the big scissors
Roughly running at the beach
No one dare fighting with me

舉起大大剪刀
橫行霸道在沙灘上遊走
誰敢與我爭鬥

張 鈊淳
Chang Hsin-Chun
age 8　Female
Taiwan（台湾／高雄）

大きなハサミを持ちあげて
砂浜を自分勝手に走りまわり
おれと戦うやつなんていないさ

Fire colored caterpillar
Almost turning in cocoon
It is windy, but it does not fall

Lagarta cor de fogo
Quase virando casulo
Venta mas não cai

Ana Clara Santos de Freitas
age 9　Female
Brazil（ブラジル）

火のような色のイモムシ
もうすぐさなぎになる
風は強いけれど落ちない

The dragonfly
Stuck in a bubble
His life is rocking

La libellule
Coincée dans une bulle
Sa vie bascule

Aissatou-Fary Ndiaye
age13　Female
Senegal（セネガル）

トンボ
泡のなかに閉じこめられて
ゆれる暮らし

The butterfly flies
Where the moonlight
Indicates the path

A borboleta voa
Por onde o luar
Lhe indica o caminho

Filipa Westwood Duarte Camacho Quadrio
age 9　Female
Portugal（ポルトガル）

チョウが
飛んでいく
月明かりに導かれて

ピクニックで
お腹(なか)をいっぱいにしている
アリたちだ!

At the picnic
Filling their bellies
There are the ants!

No piquenique
Enchendo a barriga
Estão as formigas!

Jean Rafael Guilovski Wojik
age12　Male
Brazil（ブラジル）

Fish in aquarium
Like playing tag
And hide and seek

Ryby w akwarium
Lubią bawić się w berka
I w chowanego

Mateusz Szupryczyński
age10　Male
Poland（ポーランド）

水槽の魚鬼ごっこやかくれんぼしているみたい

Underneath the loti, fishes are floricking
Bubbles are rising up while scales are flashing
Suddenly, fishes leap out of the water as if they are flying

鱼戏莲叶间
水汽翻腾银光现
跃然出水面

李 籽筠
Li Zijun
age10　Female
China（中国／上海）

飛びはねる魚蓮の花の周りを魚が泳ぎまわりパッと水面に飛びだした

Longing to see . . .
Longing to talk . . .
We are born

三善 優花
Yuka Miyoshi
age 8　Female
Japan（日本）

会いたくてお話ししたくて生まれたよ

At dawn, so small, so beautiful
His colors enchant the sky
It's a butterfly

A l'aube, si petit, si beau
Ses couleurs enchantent le ciel
C'est un papillon

Mame Saye Ndiaye
age15　Female
Senegal（セネガル）

夜明けにかくも小さく美しく
その色が空を魅了する
それはチョウ

In the heat of the sun
The ladybugs are flying
My garden grows

Al calor del sol
Vuelan las mariquitas
Mi huerto crece

Eva Minaya Perales
age11　Female
Spain（スペイン）

お日さまの暖かさのなかで
てんとう虫が飛んでいる
わたしの庭が茂る

Cheer up, cheer up
Little red crabs
Good sumo wrestlers

計屋 美羽
Miu Hakariya
age 6　Female
Japan（日本）

はっけよい
おすもうじょうず
あかがにさん

雨の後の涼しい日
春の花ざかり虫は飛ぶ
にぎやかなケロケロ

A cool day after the rain
Flowery sping day with bugs flying
The thriving sound of croaking

雨后凉爽天
春满花开昆虫飞
鸣声响满园

李 双双
Li Shuangshuang
age14　Female
China（中国／上海）

A beautiful day
And colorful butterfly
And frog ate it

Allen Nicj Sahador
age14　Male
Philippines（フィリピン）

すばらしい日
きれいな色のチョウを
カエルが食べた

Early night
The frog jumps off
I want to jump too

Entrada da noite
O pula pula do sapo
Também quero pular

Nicoly Stefanovicz Siqueira
age 9　Female
Brazil（ブラジル）

夕方
カエルがジャンプする
わたしも飛びたいわ

All dressed up in green
Croaks and croaks with two bulging eyes
Bounces to catch the insects

一身绿衣裳
眼睛鼓鼓呱呱叫
捉虫蹦蹦跳

肖 芊瑶
Xiao Qianyao
age11　Female
China（中国／上海）

緑の服
目玉はくりくり
ピョンピョン虫を取る

Red flower of love
Color flowing on wings
The tender butterfly

Rouge fleur de l'amour
Couleur coulant sur des ailes
Le papillon tendre

André Debergé
age14　Male
Senegal（セネガル）

愛の赤い花
その色は羽にさらさらと
しなやかなチョウ

Voices of cicadas in school yard
Making noise in flame trees
Singing farewell song

Sân trường rộn tiếng ve
Râm ran giữa tàng cây phượng vĩ
Ve hát bài chia tay

Nguyễn Thị Uyên Minh
Nguyen Thi Uyen Minh
age13　Female
Vietnam（ベトナム）

校庭にセミの声
火炎樹のなか賑やかに
別れの歌を歌っている

The loch salmon swims
Swims against the stream
It's no effort for him

De roze zalm zwemt
Hij zwemt tegen de richting in
Het kost geen moeite

Sam Mulder
age12　Male
Netherlands（オランダ）

入り江のサケが泳ぐ
流れに逆らって泳ぐ
おちゃのこさいさい

Sea turtle
Swim slowly
Swim with me

Tortuga de mar
Nada despacio
Nada conmigo

Sayra Buitrón
age 11 Female
Ecuador（エクアドル）

ウミガメ
ゆっくり泳ぐ
わたしと泳ぐ

Turtles
Lay their eggs
Turtle cubs

Le tartarughe
Depongono le uova
Tartarughini

Giulia Pelosi
age 8 Female
Italy（イタリア）

カメが
たまごを生んだ
カメの子どもたち

A humpback whale
Is flying in the sparkling starry sky
Like having wings

大翅鯨
在閃爍的星空飛翔
好像有翅膀

曾 祥育
Tseng Hsiang-Yu
age 9 Male
Taiwan（台湾／台北）

ザトウクジラが
きらめく星空を飛んでいく
翼があるように

青い海底に
絶滅していくシロナガスクジラ
目には見えない悲しみよ

Bottom of blue sea
Vanishing blue whale
Invisible sorrow

Dưới đáy địa dương xanh
Loài cá voi sắp tuyệt chủng
Nỗi đau này ai thấy

Đào Vân Anh
Dao Van Anh
age15　Female
Vietnam（ベトナム）

青くて深い海
クラゲの群れが出かけると
流れ星が降るみたい

In deep blue sea
A flock of jellyfishes go on an outing
Just like meteoric showers

湛藍深海裡
水母成群郊遊去
好像流星雨

盧 羿溥
Lu Yi-Pu
age 8　Male
Taiwan（台湾／高雄）

Armed with just colour
Swaying and dancing around
For life or for death

Vienīgais ierocis - krāsa
Tas dejo
Dzīvībai vai nāvei

Rēzija Daniela Sarma
Rezija Daniela Sarma
age13　Female
Latvia（ラトビア）

色だけで武装して
ゆれたりぐるぐる踊ったり
生きるか死ぬか

Beautiful yellow lights
Mayflies play with lights
Happy life for an only night

แสงไฟเหลืองสวยงาม
แมลงเม่าเล่นกับแสงไฟ
ชีวิตสุขคืนเดียว

ด.ญ. พาประวีร์ ยุวนะศิริ
Paprawee Yuwanasiri
age11　Female
Thailand（タイ）

きれいな黄色の光
カゲロウが光と遊ぶ
ひと晩だけの楽しい生命

Frogs love singing
"ribbit" "ribbit" "ribbit" sang by the frogs
Everyone praise their singing

青蛙愛唱歌
一聲一聲呱呱呱
歌聲人人誇

林 裕玹
Lin Yuh-Shyuan
age 9　Male
Taiwan（台湾／高雄）

カエルは歌うのが好き
「クワッ」「クワッ」「クワッ」と歌うと
みんながほめる

A roly poly
Holding his sides
With laughter

建部 百音
Mone Tatebe
age 7　Female
Japan（日本）

だんごむし
はらをかかえて
わらってる

だんごむし
はらをかかえて
わらってる

Frogs are crying loudly
Happily, Dad and I listen to them
Concert in the midst of the field

เสียงกบเขียดเซ็งแซ่
พ่อกับฉันนอนฟังสุขใจ
ดนตรีกลางทุ่งนา

ด.ญ.ลักษิกา ลาหลายเลิศ
Laksika　Lalailirt
age12　Female
Thailand（タイ）

カエルが大きな声で鳴く
うれしくて父さんと耳をすます
田んぼのなかのコンサート

Bottom of the well
Why the sky so small
Questioning the frog

Chú ếch ngồi đáy giếng
Chú ta thường hay hỏi tại sao
Bầu trời lại bé thế

Đặng Nhật Minh
Dang Nhat Minh
age11　Male
Vietnam（ベトナム）

井のなかのカエル
いつも考えている
どうして空は小さいの

The green turtle in the sea
Diving with me to take an adventure
What a beautiful sea world

大海綠蠵龜
陪我浮潛去探險
美麗海世界

錢 宥云
Chen Yu-Yun
age10　Female
Taiwan（台湾／高雄）

海のなかのアオウミガメ
わたしと一緒にダイビング
なんてきれいな海の世界

In the swimming pool
I do feel like a penguin
And I do swim as one

In het zwembad
Ik voel me als een pinguin
En zo zwem ik ook

Imaura van der Werff
age 6　Female
Netherlands（オランダ）

プールで
ペンギンになったきがする
ほんとにペンギンみたいにおよぐ

The snail crawls slowly complaining of its clumsiness
The mushroom asks where you are going to
I envy you can crawl

ทากคลานช้าบ่นท้อ
เห็ดถามว่าเธอจะไปไหน
อิจฉาจังคลานได

Phantipa Imorachorn
age14　Female
Thailand（タイ）

のろいとブツブツ言いながらカタツムリは進む
キノコが聞いた、君はどこへ行くの
動ける君がうらやましい

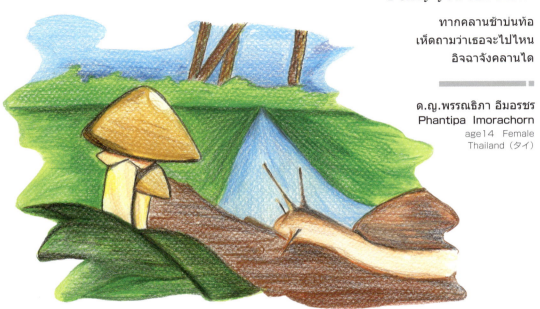

Dark evening
A spider between trees
Weaving dreams

Tamsus vakaras
Tarp medžių voras audžia
Sapnų gaudyklę

Leonardas Orlakas
age14　Male
Lithuania（リトアニア）

暗い夜
木々のあいだのクモ
夢を編む

Red spotted armour
Scuttles away from the rain
Delicate creature

Elsa Priest
age 8　Female
UK（英国）

点々つきの赤いよろい
雨をよけて急ぎ足
デリケートな生きもの

3章 だいちとともに
With Mother Earth

さくらの花
夕日にきれい
風と踊っている

Cherry blossom tree
Beautiful in the sunset
Dancing with the wind

Ethan Emmanuel Hock Zun Hao
age 7　Male
Singapore（シンガポール）

In the heart of a seed, buried so deep
A dear little plant
Lay fast asleep

Sonam Tenzin Dorji
age 9　Male
Bhutan（ブータン）

種の真んなかに深く埋もれて
小さな植物が
横になってぐっすり寝てる

Trees reaching the sky
I can climb shaking branches
Standing up with pride

Andrew Lee
age 9　Male
USA（米国／サンディエゴ）

空へ届く木
枝をゆらしながら登って
得意顔

Humans, oh, humans
Their different coloured hands
Love the life you live

Ellie Greary
age13　Female
Ireland（アイルランド）

人間、ああ人間よ
さまざまな色の手
あなたの人生を愛しなさい

Don't pick flower
Don't kill any life
They all are the same

नटिप्नु फुल
नमार्नु जीव जन्तु
सबै एक हुन्

आर्या ढुङ्गेल
Aarya Dhungel
age15　Female
Nepal（ネパール）

花を取らないで
生命をけさないで
みな同じひとつの生命

The snowy sky
Falls down onto my palm
Melts on my hands

Lumine taevas
Langeb mu peopesale
Sulab mu kätel

Marie Teppart
age13　Female
Estonia（エストニア）

雪空
手のひらに舞いおりて
手のなかで溶ける

I wake up today
With my heart still beating
I love my good life!

Juan Lucas Sumadsad
age 7　Male
Canada（カナダ）

今日目がさめると
ぼくの心臓が脈打っている
生きているってすばらしい！

The lake is quiet
Only the sound of flies
On this summer day

Sjön är helt stilla
Man hör flugorna surra
I sommardagen

Edvin Wiklund
age12　Male
Sweden（スウェーデン）

静かな湖
ただハエの羽音
この夏の日

A cold lightless night
The trees whispering softly
Dancing gracefully

Gabriel G. De Ungria
age13　Male
Philippines（フィリピン）

寒くて暗い夜
木々はそっとささやき
しなやかに踊る

Animals are hibernating
I can't
I have to go to school

Die Tiere haben Winterschlaf
Ich kann nicht
Ich muß zur Schule

Katharina Shi
age12　Female
Germany（ドイツ）

動物は冬眠
私は
学校へ

Day to day, I see you
The day you were cut down
Dear tree, good bye

Dag til dag, ser deg
Den dagen ble du hogget
Kjære tre, ha det

Dilhumar Abuduryim
age12　Female
Norway（ノルウェー）

毎日毎日、木を眺めていた
切りたおされるその日まで
愛する木よ、さようなら

Me in the morning
My eyes see
Miracles of universe

Өглөө босоод би
Эртөнцийн гайхамшгийг
Нүдээрээ хардаг

Энжин Сэндэр
Enkhjin Sender
age11　Female
Mongolia（モンゴル）

朝のわたし
わたしの目は
宇宙の奇跡を見る

Red and white roses
They have different colours
But still they have thorns

Niccolette May Adriatico
age11　Female
Singapore（シンガポール）

赤と白のバラ
色はちがっても
トゲがある

The moon sets, the sun rises
The color of the earth shines
Lost ghosts found their owners

Саран дуусч наран эхлэхэд
Дэлхийн өнгө сэргэж
Төөрсөн сүнснүүд эзнээ олно

Цэдэндорж Бат-Оргил
Tsedendorj Bat-Orgil
age13　Male
Mongolia（モンゴル）

月が沈み日が昇る
世界の色が輝くと
迷える霊たちはその主を見つけた

Interesting creatures
All around me. I worry
They are afraid of me

Zanimiva bitja
Me obkrožajo
Skrbi me, da se me bojijo

Eva Ziherl
age11　Female
Slovenia（スロベニア）

おもしろい生きものたちが
わたしを取りかこんでいる
わたしを怖がっていないか心配

Flowers in the soil
Tickles me in many ways
Flowers make me smile

Benjamin Wong En Kai
age 5　Male
Singapore（シンガポール）

じめんにさくはな
いろんなふうにくすぐるよ
はなをみてにっこり

緑(みどり)の茂(しげ)り
心地(ここち)よい鳥(とり)のさえずり
美(うつく)しい自然(しぜん)

Green flora
Melodious bird chirping
Beautiful nature

Flora menghijau
Burung berkicau merdu
Indahnya alam

Loh Yun Qi
age12　Female　Malaysia（マレーシア）

ひと粒の種をまく
ニュートンのリンゴの木が
心のなかで大きく育つ

Sowing a seed
Of Newton's apple tree
Growing in my mind

撒一粒种子
种棵牛顿苹果树
在心中长大

王 冠琳
Wang Guanlin
age10　Female　China（中国／天津）

On a spring day
Dandelion weathers invite you to
Make wreaths of flowers

Võillilleilmad
Kutsuvad kevadpäeval
Pärgi punuma

Kärola Sologub
Karola Sologub
age 8　Female
Estonia（エストニア）

春の日の
タンポポ日和が誘う
花冠づくり

Living things
Towards the development
The life is about to die

Амьтай бүхэн
Хөгжил рүү тэмүүлсээр
Амьдрал мөхсөөр...

Отгонсүрэн Гантөгөлдөр
Otgonsuren Gantuguldur
age10　Male
Mongolia（モンゴル）

生きものたち
成長して
やがて死んでいく

Like puzzle pieces
All tied to the big picture
God's ultimate art

Christopher I Kashimoto
age14　Male
USA（米国／ハワイ）

パズルのピースのように
すべてつながって大きな絵になる
神さまの最高の芸術

Don't look from physical
But look at yourself
How rare and precious you are

Natasha Insan Wibowo
age14　Female
Indonesia（インドネシア）

見た目で決めつけないで
どれだけ珍しくて大切かって
思ってごらん

Green, tall, flexible
Rustling, swaying with the wind
Totem pole of luck

Adrian Beltran
age13　Male
USA（米国／グアム）

緑色で背が高くてしなやか
ざわざわと風にゆれる
幸運のトーテムポール

Freckled angry girl
Is the princess of spring
With her green tiara

Çilli kızgın kız
Baharın prensesidir
Yeşil tacıyla

Elif Eylül Tütüncü
age11　Female
Turkey（トルコ）

まっ赤におこった
そばかす娘は　春のプリンセス
緑のティアラをつけて

夏がきて
あたたかくなると
みんなのんびり

Summer comes
The warmth starts
People get relaxed

Зун болж
Халуун дулаан эхэлж
Хүмүүс амарна

Баярсайхан Мөнх-Эрдэнэ
Bayarsaikhan Munkh-Erdene
age10　Male
Mongolia（モンゴル）

A long time ago
Gigantic feet
Had walked around

津守 陽
Hinata Tsumori
age 9　Male
Japan（日本）

おおむかし
大きな足が
歩いたよ

Been living for centuries
I, the old sycamore tree
Home for living things

Asırlardır yaşarım
Yaşlı çınarım
Canlılara yuvayım

İnci Saracik
age12　Female
Turkey（トルコ）

何百年も生きる
わたしは年老いたプラタナス
わたしは生きものたちの住みか

Me, mother's daughter
Mother, nature's daughter
We, children of nature

Би ээжийн охин
Ээж байгалийн охин
Бид байгалийн үрс

Эрдэнэхүү Наранхишиг
Erdenekhuu Narankhishig
age11　Female
Mongolia（モンゴル）

わたしは母の娘
母は自然の娘
わたしたちは自然の子ども

Branches on a tree
Still grow though the seasons change
Determination

Zachary TN Clissold
age14　Male
USA（米国／ハワイ）

木の枝は
季節が変わってもまだ伸びつづける
決心

The rippled water
my life choices it reflects,
ever shifting thoughts

The rippled water
My life choices it reflects
Ever shifting thoughts

Tara Preeya Nair
age10　Female
Singapore（シンガポール）

さざ波
わたしのくるくる変わる思いを
うつしている

Sunny Sunday
My friends at the pool
Look like mermaids

Domingo de sol
Minhas amigas na piscina
Parecem sereias

Thaís Drewnowski
age 6　Female
Brazil（ブラジル）

ぴかぴかのにちようび
プールのともだち
にんぎょひめみたい

Do not open the hanging roll!
A bird may fly away from it
Be careful of your eyes

别打开画轴
那鸟儿会飞出来
小心你的眼

周 立言
Zhou Liyan
age11　Male
China（中国／天津）

掛け軸をひらかないで
鳥が飛びだしそう
目に気をつけて

A winter day, with heavy snow
Giving sweet dessert for people, precious food for birds
Our thin and bare persimmon tree, aren't you cold?

눈이 펑펑 내리는 추운 겨울에
우리에게는 달콤한 감을, 산비둘기에게는 소중한 양식을 주고
헐거벗은 우리집 감나무야! 춥지는 않니?

김 민서
Kim Minseo
age12　Female
Korea（韓国）

大雪の日
人には甘いデザートを、鳥にはエサを
裸になった柿の木よ、大丈夫？

On the Double-ninth Festival
The petals of the chrysanthemums in Huangzhou
Are scattering in the sky full of golden light

黃州菊花絕
重陽時節花瓣飛
金光佈滿天

李 子筠
Li Tzu-Yun
age14　Female
Taiwan（台湾／台北）

重陽の節句
黄州では菊の花びらが
金色の光あふれる空に舞いちる

Dandelion
The pon pon slowly descends
No wind at all

Dente de leão
O pompom desce devagarinho
Sem vento nenhum

Vitória Amanda Rennó Zarpellon
age10　Female
Brazil（ブラジル）

タンポポ
綿毛がゆっくり降りていく
まったく風がない

Lilly pad floating
On the river of my dreams
What is my future？

Piper Baker
age12　Female
UK（英国）

睡蓮の葉が
私の夢の川に浮かぶ
未来はどんな？

Flowers blooming in the garden
Butterflies and bees flying close to them
Each flower is beautiful like fairy

花園花開也
蝴蝶蜜蜂朵朵親
朵朵如仙子

張　昱翔
Chang Yu-Hsiang
age12　Male
Taiwan（台湾／高雄）

庭に花が咲いている
花にキスしてまわるチョウとハチ
妖精のように美しい花々

宇宙から
キリンがみたら ひとは
まるで アリンコ

Giraffe from space
Look at the people
Just like ants

Baktı uzaydan
İnsanlara zürafa
Aynı karınca

Petek Çakici
age13　Female
Turkey（トルコ）

I wonder how I came on this Earth
But when I see stars twinkling
I feel I am also a star

मैं सोचु मैं कैसे आया इस धरती पर
मैं देखु तारो को कैसे टमिटमिाते तारे
सोचु मैं भी हू एक तार

Zoya
age 8　Female
India（インド）

わたしはどうやって地球にきたのかな
星がキラキラしてるのを見ると
わたしもお星さまだと思うの

Little sunflower,
Aren't you afraid of the dark sky?
The sun is coming soon

小小向日葵
天这么黑你怕吗
太阳快来啦

李 仁源
Li Renyuan
age 6　Male
China（中国／天津）

ちいさなヒマワリ
こんなくらいそらはこわくない？
たいようはもうすぐくるよ

Green bamboos growing innocently
People are pleased with it
Such bamboos are in my garden

青青翠竹林
虚心向上人喜爱
竹生我家园

芦 睿涵
Lu Ruihan
age11　Male
China（中国／北京）

青々とした竹が
すくすくと育つ姿はみんなに愛される
そういう竹がぼくの家の庭にある

Covered with fire and smoke
The forest is burnt down by red flame
Star gooseberries are waiting to grow

ควันไฟฟุ้งกลางป่า
แสงสีแดงแผดเผาไปทั่ว
ผักหวานรอแตกยอด

ด.ช.อดิเทพ แพรศรี
Aditep Praesri
age11　Male
Thailand（タイ）

火と煙につつまれ
森は赤い炎で焼けおちた
スグリは大きくなろうとじっと待つ

My wonderful life
Just like a blooming flower
Shining bright

Hidupku indah
Seperti bunga mekar
Memancar sinar

Intan Binti Zainal Azhar
age12　Female
Malaysia（マレーシア）

私のすばらしい生命
咲いている花のように
明るく輝く

The humble plant
Fu-chan bows
One time

久冨 蕗乃
Fukino Hisatomi
age 6　Female
Japan（日本）

おじぎそう
ふうちゃんいっかい
おじぎした

Tang tree blossoms in April, snow in May
Their glossy whiteness like the pearly luster of tears
Oh, How pure and simple love is!

四月桐花五月雪
白皙透亮的光澤似淚珠的色彩
喔~潔白單純的愛情

林 奕綺
Lin I-Chi
age13　Female
Taiwan（台湾／台北）

四月の油桐　五月の花吹雪
白くてキラキラと輝く光沢は真珠の涙
なんて愛は純粋で清らかなの

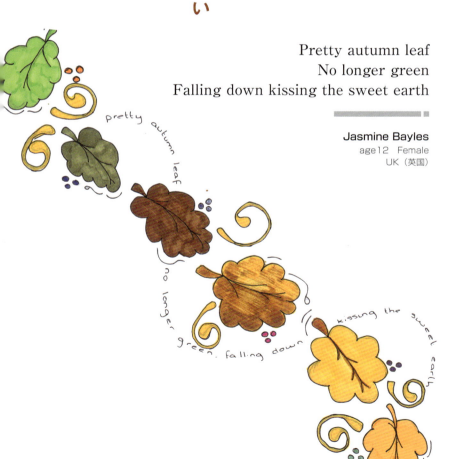

Pretty autumn leaf
No longer green
Falling down kissing the sweet earth

Jasmine Bayles
age12　Female
UK（英国）

きれいな秋の葉
もう緑色ではなく
落ちてやさしい地球にキス

Unkept and wild
With a humid warmth
My ancestors stand tall

Jayna Rose C. Cruz
age11 Female
USA(米国/グアム)

ほったらかしで自然
湿ったあたたかさのなか
自信を持って立つわたしの祖先

White clouds, cotton!
Spring is here
And the sun is shinning

Nubes blancos ¡algodón!
La primavera llega y
El sol brilla

Juan José Iribarren Sánchez
age 8　Male
Spain（スペイン）

白い雲、綿だ！
春になり
お日さまが輝く

The fragrance of flowers brushes through my face
Guarding the flowers by wind, rain and my heart
Trying to keep the fragrance stay

花兒拂面香
隨風隨雨隨心來守護
徒此挹清芳

張 銘禎
Chang Ming-Chen
age12　Female
Taiwan（台湾／高雄）

花の香りが顔をなでてゆく
風と雨と私の心が花を守る
香りがとどまるように

God's creation
Humans and nature
Need each other

Ciptaan tuhan
Manusia serta alam
Saling memerlu

Muhammad Luqman Hakim Bin Turijan
age12　Male
Malaysia（マレーシア）

神さまの創造物
人と自然
お互いが必要

庭の木々
村には大きな学校
村に秋がやってきた

Trees in the garden
A big school in our village
Autumn has come to the village

Այգում կան ծառեր.
Մեր գյուղում կա մեծ դպրոց
Գյուղում աշուն է.

Գևորգյան Վիոլետա
Gevorgyan Violeta
age 9　Female
Armenia（アルメニア）

How does a tree know when the season change?
Let's ask the tree
For the tree is wise

나무는 어떻게 계절을 알고 나뭇잎을 떨어뜨리거나 색을 바꿀까
나무에게 물어보자
나무는 똑똑하니까

どうやってきせつをしるの？
きにきいてみよう
きはかしこいから

조 혜원
Cho Hyewon
age 6　Female
Korea（韓国）

The wheat stalks whisper
Like students in a classroom
A tree teaches them

麦の茎がささやく
教室の生徒たちのように
一本の木が先生

Ayushi Sanadhya
age12　Female
India（インド）

Flowers bloom
Like singing birds
With happiness

Flores desabrocham
Como as aves a cantar
Com felicidade

花がひらく
幸せそうに歌う
鳥たちのように

Gonçalo Nelso
age13　Male
Portugal（ポルトガル）

山の桜が満開
ひろい花の海に
花の香りがあふれる

The cherry blossoms flourish all over the mountain
In the boundless sea of flowers
Overflowed with the fragrance of flowers

櫻花開滿山
一望無際的花海
花兒撲鼻香

蘇 霈
Su Pei
age11　Female
Taiwan（台湾／高雄）

ほとんど葉っぱはなくとも
とがった枝(えだ)は生(い)き生(い)きと
水滴(すいてき)を吸(す)っている

Barely sprouting leaves
Prickly branches striving
Absorbing droplets

Ellaya Thompson
age 9　Female
Australia（オーストラリア）

遠足(えんそく)で豫園(よえん)へ
緑(みどり)の竹(たけ)と美(うつく)しい蓮(はす)の葉(は)っぱ
翡翠(ひすい)のよう

Outing to the Yu Garden
Green bamboos and beautiful lotus leaves
Jade-like lotus leaves

周游至豫园
但见绿筱媚青莲
娇荷似玉璇

周 筱璇
Zhou Xiaoxuan
age11　Female
China（中国／上海）

ぼくのうち
たんけんしてる
おにやんま

In my house
Exploring around
The giant dragonfly

長田 来唯
Rai Osada
age 6　Male
Japan（日本）

世界は生き生き
音や色にかこまれていると
楽しくなる

World is alive
Among sounds, colours
I'm happy to be

Pasaulis gyvas
Garsų, spalvų, apsupty
Gera gyventi

Ūla Kaukėnaitė
Ula Kaukenaite
age13　Female
Lithuania（リトアニア）

JAL財団では日本の伝統文化である俳句創作の楽しさを世界の子どもたちに広め、日本への理解と国際交流を促進するために「世界こどもハイクコンテスト」を一九九〇年より開催しています。世界の子どもたちによるハイク創作は近年ますますその輪が広がり、厚みが増しています。今回も新たにブータン、ブルガリア、エクアドル、ノルウェー、ポーランド、スリランカから多くの作品が寄せられましたが、これまで十五回にわたるコンテストには、今回の二万五千作品を含めて合計七十万もの作品が世界五十七の国と地域から寄せられています。

このコンテストの特徴は、「五・七・五」の日本語で表される日本の俳句本来の姿とは異なり、世界の子どもたちがそれぞれの国の言葉を使って「三行詩」でさまざまな情景やそこから得た感動を表現しているところ、そして、それを自らが描いた絵とともに作品にしていることにあります。子どもたちのみずみずしい感性がそのまま言葉と絵で表現されており、大人の私たちが思わず〝はっと〟させられ新たな感動を覚えたり、〝にっこり〟と温かい気持ちにさせられるような作品の数々です。

さて、昨今私たちの周りでも日本社会のグローバル化の必要性とともに、ダイバーシティー（多様性）の受容を求める声が多く聞かれるようになりました。環境問題、さまざまな価値観のぶつかり合い、他者への非寛容等々の問題が地球の将来へのリスクとして大きく取り上げられています。世界が「持続可能な発展」を遂げていくためには、次代を担う青少年たちが互いの違いを認め合い、あるべき未来の姿に向かって国境の枠を超えて協力し合っていくことが必要であろうと感じます。

世界中から集まった作品の数々の中には、子どもたちが日常生活の中で目にしている情景が表現されていますが、同じような日常のシーンであっても、それぞれの国によって見え方、感じ方もさまざまなのだということを感じとられた方もいらっしゃるのではないでしょうか。ハイクと絵の創作を通して、世界の子どもたちが繋がり、そしてそれぞれの違いに気づき、それを認め合う。「世界こどもハイクコンテスト」が日本文化の海外への紹介だけではなく、地球の将来を担う青少年の国際理解へと繋がっていけば、このコンテストを実施していただいている私どもにとっても大変嬉しく、ありがたいことだと思います。

終わりにあたり、このコンテストの開催に多大なるご支援をくださいました国際俳句交流協会、国際交流基金、日本ユニセフ協会、各国大使館、外務省・在外公館、文化庁、ブロンズ新社、日本航空などの皆さまへ、心より御礼を申し上げます。

公益財団法人JAL財団
常務理事　田中　順二

＊第十六回「世界こどもハイクコンテスト」は、二〇一九年に「スポーツ」をテーマに開催する予定です。世界中の子どもたちからの作品をお待ちしています。詳細は、公益財団法人JAL財団のホームページ（http://www.jal-foundation.or.jp）をご覧下さい。

おわりに

Epilogue

The JAL Foundation has held the World Children's Haiku Contest since 1990 to spread the fun of writing haiku, a Japanese traditional culture, to children worldwide and to promote the understanding of Japan and international exchanges. In recent years, the art of haiku has expanded its global popularity among children both in breadth and depth. In the latest contest, we received many works from new participating countries such as Bhutan, Bulgaria, Ecuador, Norway, Poland and Sri Lanka, bringing the aggregate total of haiku received from 57 countries and regions in the total 15 contests to 700,000, including the recent 25,000 entries.

The special aspects of this contest are that the haiku works consist of three lines, differing from the 5-7-5 syllable count of traditional Japanese haiku, and are written in the children's mother tongue. The topics are local scenes and impressions, and a picture is drawn to go with the haiku. The children's fresh, young sensitivity shines through their words and stuns and touches adults, warming their hearts and making them smile when they read them.

There has been much discussion in recent years, even around us, regarding the need for globalization and acceptance of diversity in Japanese society. Environmental problems, clashes between differing values, intolerance of other people and other issues pose a serious risk to the future of the earth. To achieve sustainable development across the globe, I feel that it is essential that the next generation respects and accepts differences and promotes cross-border cooperation to realize a more prosperous future.

The haiku works sent to the JAL Foundation from around the world depict scenes from the daily life of children. However, you will discover that different countries and cultures interpret the same scene differently. Haiku and drawings connect children around the world and encourage them to understand and accept differences in others. As the organizer of the World Children's Haiku Contest, we would be more than happy and thankful if the contest could contribute to introducing Japanese culture overseas and lead to international understanding among today's youth, who will shape the next generation.

In closing, I would like to express my sincere appreciation to the Haiku International Association, the Japan Foundation, the Japan Committee for UNICEF, embassies in each country, the Ministry of Foreign Affairs of Japan, diplomatic missions abroad, the Agency for Cultural Affairs, Bronze Publishing Inc., Japan Airlines and many other entities for their significant support and cooperation in making this contest possible.

Junji Tanaka
Managing Director
JAL Foundation

The 16th "World Children's Haiku Contest" will be held in 2019 under the theme of "Sports". We look forward to seeing haiku from children all over the world. For more details, please visit the JAL Foundation website. (http://www.jal-foundation.or.jp)

44 の国・地域 ──────── 44 countries and regions

Netherlands　オランダ
Noor Baljeu　23
Sam Mulder　47
Imaura van der Werff　53

Norway　ノルウェー
Dilhumar Abuduryim　59

Philippines　フィリピン
Allen Nicj Sahador　46
Gabriel G. De Ungria　58

Poland　ポーランド
Dominika Musiał　14
Zuzanna Formanowska　27
Mateusz Szupryczyński　43

Portugal　ポルトガル
Eliane Augusta Monteiro Semedo　20
Filipa Westwood Duarte Camacho Quadrio　41
Gonçalo Nelso　76
Tomás Oliveira Guerreiro Reis　81, 84

Romania　ルーマニア
Mambet Esra　36

Russia　ロシア
Anastasia Pilyuginae　33

Senegal　セネガル
Rin Okayasu　22
Aissatou-Fary Ndiaye　40
Mame Saye Ndiaye　44
André Debergé　47

Singapore　シンガポール
Charlotte Tham　7
Tong Wan Ying　15
Hannah Tang　26
Chew En Hui, Stephanie　30
Ethan Emmanuel Hock Zun Hao　55
Niccolette May Adriatico　59
Benjamin Wong En Kai　60
Tara Preeya Nair　67

Slovenia　スロベニア
Nastja Marčič　11
Galen Gaberščeek　16
Gregor Klobučar　29
Eva Ziherl　60

Spain　スペイン
Pablo Tébar Medina　15
Carolina Guantes Domínguez　19
Irene Ochando Jiménez　21
Ana Torres Molina　23
Nuria García Acejo　28
Eva Minaya Perales　44
Juan José Iribarren Sánchez　74

Sri Lanka　スリランカ
M. Pethmin Sasen Rodrigo　5
T.G.Noshika Ganguli　17

Sweden　スウェーデン
Edvin Wiklund　58

Taiwan　台湾（高雄・台北）
Chang Tzu-Fei　7
Chu Ting-Yi　9
Li Yi-Lun　13
Chang Hsin-Chun　40
Tseng Hsiang-Yu　48
Lu Yi-Pu　50
Lin Yuh-Shyuan　51
Chen Yu-Yun　53
Li Tzu-Yun　68
Chang Yu-Hsiang　69
Lin I-Chi　72
Chang Ming-Chen　74
Su Pei　77

Thailand　タイ
Paprawee Yuwanasiri　51
Laksika Lalailirt　52
Phantipa Imorachorn　54
Aditep Praesri　71

Turkey　トルコ
Eylül Yener　19
Emirhan Akyol　32
Elif Eylül Tütüncü　64

İnci Saracik　66
Petek Çakici　70

UK　英国
Felix Dewsnap　8
Joshua Das　26
Rafe Dewsnap　34
Elsa Priest　54
Piper Baker　69
Jasmine Bayles　72

USA　米国（ボストン／シカゴ／ダラス／グアム／ハワイ／ロサンゼルス／ニューヨーク／サンディエゴ）
Orion Hall　8
Akio Calvin Richard Freauff　10
Audrey Lin　16
Drew Hesp　31
Andrew Lee　56
Christopher I Kashimoto　63
Adrian Beltran　64
Zachary TN Clissold　66
Jayna Rose C. Cruz　73

Vietnam　ベトナム
Luu Bao Khoi　8
Tran Thanh Ngan　15
Nguyen Gia Linh　27
Tran Thuc Anh　28
Nguyen Yen Trang　32
Nguyen Thi Uyen Minh　47
Dao Van Anh　49
Dang Nhat Minh　52

INDEX

Armenia アルメニア
Gevorgyan Violeta　75

Australia オーストラリア
Ellaya Thompson　78

Bhutan ブータン
Sonam Tenzin Dorji　56

Brazil ブラジル
Camila Aparecida Gaiocha　39
Ana Clara Santos de Freitas　40
Jean Rafael Guilovski Wojik　42
Nicoly Stefanovicz Siqueira　46
Thaís Drewnowski　67
Vitória Amanda Rennó Zarpellon　69

Bulgaria ブルガリア
Gabriela Spasova Zasheva　2,84
Desislava Tsvetanova Dimitrova　6
Raya Venkova Moyankova　16
Elena Svetlanova Deyanova　39

Canada カナダ
Juan Lucas Sumadsad　57

China 中国(北京／大連／広州／香港／上海／天津)
Cheung Pak Man　裏表紙/Back Cover
Siu Cheuk Hei Matt　12
Qu Yihan　35
Zhang Xinjie　37
Li Zijun　43
Li Shuangshuang　45
Xiao Qianyao　46
Wang Guanlin　62
Zhou Liyan　67
Li Renyuan　70
Lu Ruihan　71
Zhou Xiaoxuan　78

Croatia クロアチア
Ela Makic Halilcevic　7
Antonio Frljuzec　11
Marko Sepic　24

Ecuador エクアドル
Nariaty Andrade　扉/Front Page,84
Sayra Buitrón　48

Estonia エストニア
Sandra Roos　19
Marie Teppart　57
Karola Sologub　63

Finland フィンランド
Eeva Kari　12

France フランス
Wayne Fatimata　14
Glan Orlane　24
Lebon Shanna　36

Germany ドイツ
Cornelius Dort　32
Katharina Shi　58

India インド
Shivam　34
Zoya　70
Ayushi Sanadhya　76

Indonesia インドネシア
Muhammad Alive Muflih　11
Natasha Insan Wibowo　64

Ireland アイルランド
Lorraine O'Shea　13
Roísín Beazley　20
Ellie Greary　56

Italy イタリア
Letizia Cisint　33
Emma Palamin　38
Giulia Pelosi　48

Japan 日本
Sae Nishida　14
Chika Nunokawa　25
Kako Kubo　26
Sakura Miyai　36
Yuka Miyoshi　43

Miu Hakariya　44
Mone Tatebe　52
Hinata Tsumori　65
Fukino Hisatomi　72
Rai Osada　78

Korea 韓国
Lee Hojun　18
Kim Minseo　68
Cho Hyewon　76

Latvia ラトビア
Jekaterina Krupnova　12
Darja Ginko　28
Elizabete Brale　30
Rezija Daniela Sarma　51

Lithuania リトアニア
William Schablovski　表紙/Front Cover
Matas Zajauskas　13
Rusne Rimselyte　16
Egilija Rimkute　23
Leonardas Orlakas　54
Ula Kaukenaite　79

Malaysia マレーシア
Loh Yun Qi　61
Intan Binti Zainal Azhar　71
Muhammad Luqman Hakim Bin Turijan　74

Mexico メキシコ
Ariadna Guadalupe Morales Miendeta　19
Luna Anais Campos Ruiz　26

Mongolia モンゴル
Byambadorj Dulguun-Erdene　27
Tumur Badmaarag　30
Enkhjin Sender　59
Tsedendorj Bat-Orgil　60
Otgonsuren Gantuguldur　63
Bayarsaikhan Munkh-Erdene　65
Erdenekhuu Narankhishig　66

Nepal ネパール
Anugya Nepal　12
Sushant Neupane　20
Aarya Dhungel　57

扉／Front Page			
ゆっくりゆっくり進む ゾウガメ 焼ける太陽の下で	Slowly slowly goes The giant turtle In the blazing sun	Lenta lenta va La tortuga gigante En el sol ardiente	**Nariaty Andrade** age10　Female　Ecuador（エクアドル）

はじめに／Prologue			
そして再び感じる あたたかい 春の訪れ	And I felt again The warmth of The coming spring	И отново усетих Топлината На идващата пролет	**Габриела Спасова Зашева** Gabriela Spasova Zasheva age14　Female　Bulgaria（ブルガリア）

おわりに／Epilogue			
きれいなクジャクが 庭を散歩していた なんて美しい色でしょう	A beautiful peacock Is strolling around in the garden What beautiful colors	Um pavão lindo Passeava no jardim Que cores lindas	**Tomás Oliveira Guerreiro Reis** age 8　Male　Portugal（ポルトガル）

地球歳時記
いきもののうた
Impressions of Living Things

2018年11月25日　初版第1刷発行

編　者　公益財団法人JAL財団

装　丁　籾山真之(snug.)
編　集　籾山伸子(snug.)
発行者　若月眞知子
発行所　ブロンズ新社
　　　　東京都渋谷区神宮前6-31-15-3B
　　　　03-3498-3272
　　　　http://www.bronze.co.jp/

印　刷　吉原印刷
製　本　難波製本

©2018 JAL FOUNDATION
ISBN978-4-89309-652-4 C8076

本書に掲載されている、全ての文章及び画像等の無断転用を禁じます。